This Walker book belongs to:

_____

_____

_____

First published 1988 and 2004 in *Out and About*
and *Olly and Me* by Walker Books Ltd
87 Vauxhall Walk, London SE11 5HJ

This edition published 2016

2 4 6 8 10 9 7 5 3 1

© 1988, 2004 Shirley Hughes

The right of Shirley Hughes to be identified as author/illustrator of this work
has been asserted by her in accordance with the Copyright, Designs and Patents Act 1988

This book has been typeset in Plantin Light Educational

Printed in China

British Library Cataloguing in Publication Data:
a catalogue record for this book is available from the British Library

ISBN 978-1-4063-7280-9

www.walker.co.uk

THE NURSERY
COLLECTION
SPRING

WALKER BOOKS
AND SUBSIDIARIES
LONDON • BOSTON • SYDNEY • AUCKLAND

Out and About

Shiny boots,
Brand new,
Pale shoots
Poking through.
In the garden,
Out and about,
Run down the path,
Scamper and shout.
Wild white washing
Waves at the sky,
The birds are busy
And so am I.

Mudlarks

I like mud.
The slippy, sloppy, squelchy kind,

The slap-it-into-pies kind.

Stir it up in puddles,
Slither and slide.

I *do* like mud.

Wet

Dark clouds,
Rain again,
Rivers on the
Misted pane.
Wet umbrellas
In the street,
Running noses,
Damp feet.

Pancakes

When Mum goes out and Dad looks after us, we often do cooking. Making pancakes with Dad is quite exciting. He cracks open the eggs and Olly and I help him stir up the sticky stuff. Then Dad does the frying.

The most exciting part is when he picks up the pan and flips the pancake into the air and catches it. It is even more exciting when he misses and some of the pancake goes on the floor.

Our dog Buster likes that. But eating pancakes rolled up with plenty of honey is the part we like best of all.

Spring Greens

Bulbs in pots,

Twigs in jars,

Dads in the street, washing cars.

Greens in season,

Trees in bud,

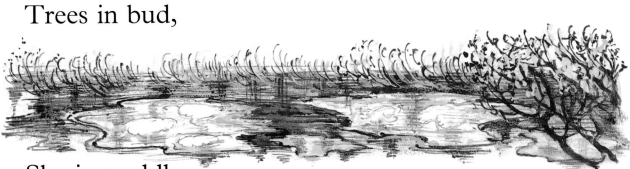

Sky in puddles,

Ripples in mud.

Birds in the bushes, singing loud.

Sun tucked up in a bed of cloud.

Hill

Huge clouds
Slowly pass;
Huge hill
Made of grass.
Jungle under,
Thick and green,
Tangled stalks
Creep between;
Scramble up,
Hug the ground…

Suddenly see
All around!
Watch out, fences,
Fields and town!
From the top of the world
I come rolling down.

My Friend Betty

There's a place in the park where the farm
animals live: the pig with a house of his own,
and the hens and geese. But whenever we
go there, I always visit Betty the sheep first.

She has a nice fat back. And when she sees me she always turns her head and lets me touch her nose.

Olly likes rabbits. When they come out of their hutch we're allowed to stroke them – the beautiful black one, the brown ones with silky ears and the white one with pink eyes.

But Betty is my special friend.